A Journal for Couples

OUR BUCKET LIST

Create Your Dream Life Together and
Record Your Adventures

l♥vitynote

this
Journal

BELONGS TO:

_____ & _____

Introduction

When it comes to living life as a couple to the fullest, setting your mutual goals and building your bucket list is of great importance. Creating your bucket list is a bonding experience in itself, but pursuing and accomplishing your goals seals that bond with a peerless sense of togetherness.

The starting point to creating the perfect bucket list is thinking about your dreams and wishes in addition to the experiences you want to share with each other. Once ready, this list will be the compass to your life journey and will motivate you to put ongoing effort toward your goals.

Next on the list is making a detailed plan that includes the actions needed to reach your goals, as well as the hindrances you may encounter along the way and how to overcome them. That will ensure you'll always stay encouraged, focused, and on track.

Executing is the final step to checking items off your list. Making sure you both work toward at least one goal on a daily basis is the key to unlocking the life you dream of. Even at times you can't make active efforts, including your dreams in your everyday life by visualizing or talking about them will keep the spark alive.

On the following pages, you will find over 100 bucket list ideas along with some tools to help you create your own bucket list. It can be dreamy or realistic, easy or hard, lofty or humble, but it's definitely going to be rewarding and reflective of you both. So, get ready to chase your dreams and let the journey begin!

How to Use This Book

This book is broken down into the following five parts.

(1) Bucket List Ideas
This section contains 101 inspiring bucket list ideas. Some of them are more widespread goals among couples while others are more original. Pick the ones you like and add them to your list. You can also alter them to suit your style and needs.

(2) Brainstorm Questions
In this part, you will find a few questions to help you think up your own bucket list ideas. Take some time to reflect and give an answer to each question. Then, compare your responses and let them inspire you in setting your mutual goals.

(3) Bucket List Item Index
This journal comes with an index table to keep all of your goals organized and easily accessible at any time. Once you've added an item to your bucket list, remember to fill it in on your index list next to the corresponding goal number.

(4) Your Bucket List Items
This is the biggest part of the book. It provides the space to jot down all of your bucket list items and journal about their fulfillment. There are two pages dedicated to each goal, where you can keep a record of your experiences, feelings, and thoughts. Moreover, there is extra space for being creative or sticking photos and other types of memorabilia to remind you of your shared adventures.

5 Reflection Questions
At the end of this journal, you will find a few questions regarding the completion of your bucket list and your overall experience. Use these questions to bring you closer while reminiscing and talking about some of your journey's most remarkable moments.

Bucket List Ideas

1. Dine at one of the world's ten best restaurants.

2. Explore a cave.

3. Visit a medieval town.

4. Record your favorite song in a professional studio.

5. Take astronomy courses and discover the universe together.

6. Body paint each other.

7. Take a tour of a haunted house.

8. Witness bioluminescence.

9. Create a tradition for your anniversary.

10. Practice tantric sex.

11. Investigate and solve a mystery that fascinates you both.

12. Kiss under the Northern Lights.

13. Get featured as a couple on TV or the radio.

14. Stay overnight in a castle.

15. Take part in a lantern festival.

16. Get your fortune told.

17. Spend a tech-free weekend indoors.

18. Go on a detox diet.

19. Visit the seven wonders of the modern world.

20. Learn a new language well enough to narrate your love story.

21. Save $1,000 for couple-related purposes.

22. Create a vision board for your next year together.

23. Take couples yoga classes.

24. Write a love song about you two.

25. Raise funds for a charity cause of your choice.

26. Read each other's favorite books.

27. Have a "Day in the Life" photography session.

28. Take a winery tour.

29. Cruise through the heart of your favorite river town.

30. Grow a window garden.

31. Have a limo party for two.

32. Hire a private chef for a special occasion dinner.

33. Stand under a waterfall.

34. Row boats on a lake.

35. Build your own couple workout routine.

36. Enjoy your favorite cocktails during a hot-air balloon ride.

37. Write, direct, and star in a short film.

38. Run a marathon.

39. Go on a dream vacation.

40. Take part in a game show.

41. Enrich your wardrobes with matching outfits.

42. Hire a travel agency to plan your next getaway as a surprise.

43. Go on a world cruise.

44. Build a tree house.

45. Try an ethnic cuisine from each continent.

46. Design your dream house in detail.

47. Go on a desert safari.

48. Create your own secret language.

49. Go bird-watching.

50. Declutter and redecorate your space.

51. Try a dozen new restaurants in six months.

52. Watch a solar eclipse.

53. Attend a concert of an artist you both love.

54. Take part in a treasure hunt.

55. Rent a telescope and explore the night sky.

56. Write a fairy tale inspired by your relationship.

57. Get your portrait painted.

58. Learn how to make sushi.

59. Scrapbook about your happy memories together.

60. Take archery classes.

61. Experience a luxury spa treatment for two.

62. Cycle through your hometowns on a tandem bike.

63. Get matching tattoos.

64. Swim with marine wildlife.

65. Go on a rainforest excursion.

66. Spend a romantic getaway in an exotic overwater bungalow.

67. Go to the opera.

68. Spend a night in an underwater hotel.

69. Attend a big sporting event.

70. Meet a celebrity you both admire.

71. Take a factory tour to observe your favorite product being manufactured.

72. Journal your thoughts and feelings for each other every day for a whole year.

73. Have a flight simulator experience.

74. Get a new pet.

75. Choreograph and learn the dance routine to your favorite song.

76. Look through your digital photos featuring you two and pick the best to make a photo book for each year you've been together.

77. Create a dish that either reflects your relationship vibes or just combines some of your favorite ingredients.

78. Decide on an issue that should be addressed in your community and work toward its resolution.

79. Start a social media channel or a blog about your relationship or something you both enjoy.

80. Take a volcano helicopter tour and witness lava flows from the sky.

81. Create a painting together to display on your walls.

82. Start a collection of something that both of you find inspiring or are passionate about.

83. Explore the history of each of your hometowns and visit all of their cultural attractions.

84. Visit a theme park and do all of its activities.

85. Learn a musical instrument together.

86. Visit three countries that neither of you has traveled to before.

87. Drive go-carts.

88. Put together a giant jigsaw puzzle.

89. Visit a flower farm.

90. Turn a hobby or interest you both have into a lucrative project.

91. Host a winter bonfire party.

92. Spend a night at the casino.

93. Take a sunset cruise.

94. Attend the Olympics.

95. Do a fun science project or experiment.

96. Surprise a mutual friend with something they would love.

97. Create your own board game.

98. Attend a classical music concert.

99. Witness a big city's New Year's Eve fireworks.

100. Enjoy a Bedouin dinner in the desert.

101. Take a romantic horse and carriage ride.

Brainstorm Questions

The following questions will help you brainstorm your own bucket list ideas. Reflect upon them and write your answers one after the other. Once, you've gone through them all, review your responses and discuss which of those could inspire new goals for your bucket list. You'll be amazed at how many ideas will pop up along the way!

1. Are there any hobbies you used to have but dropped?

2. What were your childhood dreams, even the silliest ones?

3. What skills do you admire others for?

4. Do you have any abilities or talents that you didn't have the chance to develop further?

5. Are there things you want to do, but have set aside for later?

6. Is there anything you've seen in movies that you always wanted to try or experience with your partner?

7. What are some unusual activities your friends or acquaintances have tried that you haven't?

8. Are there things that you haven't tried solely because they seem more difficult or expensive than you could handle or afford?

9. Imagine there is a new law that makes every activity that is not on your done-list illegal. Which ones do you regret not having tried out?

10. What gives you the chills in life?

Index

#	Bucket List Item	✓
1		☐
2		☐
3		☐
4		☐
5		☐
6		☐
7		☐
8		☐
9		☐
10		☐
11		☐
12		☐
13		☐
14		☐
15		☐
16		☐
17		☐
18		☐

Index

#	Bucket List Item	✓
19		☐
20		☐
21		☐
22		☐
23		☐
24		☐
25		☐
26		☐
27		☐
28		☐
29		☐
30		☐
31		☐
32		☐
33		☐
34		☐
35		☐
36		☐

Index

#	Bucket List Item	✓
37		☐
38		☐
39		☐
40		☐
41		☐
42		☐
43		☐
44		☐
45		☐
46		☐
47		☐
48		☐
49		☐
50		☐

Our Bucket List

01

Our Goal

Action plan

Our expectations

Date accomplished

The Story

Things we learned in the process

_____
_____
_____
_____
_____

Most cherished moment

_____
_____
_____
_____
_____

Something to Remember

02

Our Goal

Action plan

Our expectations

Date accomplished

The Story

Things we learned in the process

_____
_____
_____
_____
_____
_____

Most cherished moment

_____
_____
_____
_____
_____
_____

Something to Remember

03

Our Goal

Action plan

Our expectations

Date accomplished

The Story

Things we learned in the process

_____
_____
_____
_____
_____

Most cherished moment

_____
_____
_____
_____
_____

Something to Remember

04

Our Goal

Action plan

_____
_____
_____
_____
_____

Our expectations

_____
_____
_____
_____
_____

Date accomplished

_____

The Story

Things we learned in the process

_____
_____
_____
_____
_____
_____

Most cherished moment

_____
_____
_____
_____
_____
_____

Something to Remember

05

Our Goal

Action plan

Our expectations

Date accomplished

The Story

Things we learned in the process

_____
_____
_____
_____
_____

Most cherished moment

_____
_____
_____
_____
_____

Something to Remember

06

Our Goal

Action plan

_____
_____
_____
_____
_____

Our expectations

_____
_____
_____
_____
_____

Date accomplished

_____

The Story

Things we learned in the process

_____
_____
_____
_____
_____

Most cherished moment

_____
_____
_____
_____
_____

Something to Remember

07

Our Goal

Action plan

Our expectations

Date accomplished

The Story

Things we learned in the process

_____
_____
_____
_____
_____
_____

Most cherished moment

_____
_____
_____
_____
_____
_____

Something to Remember

08

Our Goal

Action plan

Our expectations

Date accomplished

The Story

Things we learned in the process

_____
_____
_____
_____
_____
_____

Most cherished moment

_____
_____
_____
_____
_____
_____

Something to Remember

09

Our Goal

Action plan

Our expectations

Date accomplished

The Story

Things we learned in the process

_____
_____
_____
_____
_____

Most cherished moment

_____
_____
_____
_____
_____

Something to Remember

10

Our Goal

Action plan

_____

_____

_____

_____

_____

Our expectations

_____

_____

_____

_____

_____

Date accomplished

_____

The Story

Things we learned in the process

_____
_____
_____
_____
_____
_____

Most cherished moment

_____
_____
_____
_____
_____
_____

Something to Remember

11

Our Goal

Action plan

Our expectations

Date accomplished

The Story

Things we learned in the process

_____
_____
_____
_____
_____

Most cherished moment

_____
_____
_____
_____
_____

Something to Remember

12

Our Goal

Action plan

_____
_____
_____
_____
_____

Our expectations

_____
_____
_____
_____
_____

Date accomplished

_____

The Story

Things we learned in the process

_____
_____
_____
_____
_____
_____

Most cherished moment

_____
_____
_____
_____
_____
_____

Something to Remember

13

Our Goal

Action plan

Our expectations

Date accomplished

The Story

Things we learned in the process

_____
_____
_____
_____
_____
_____

Most cherished moment

_____
_____
_____
_____
_____
_____

Something to Remember

14

Our Goal

Action plan

Our expectations

Date accomplished

The Story

Things we learned in the process

_____
_____
_____
_____
_____
_____

Most cherished moment

_____
_____
_____
_____
_____
_____

Something to Remember

15

Our Goal

Action plan

_____
_____
_____
_____
_____

Our expectations

_____
_____
_____
_____
_____

Date accomplished

_____

The Story

Things we learned in the process

_____
_____
_____
_____
_____

Most cherished moment

_____
_____
_____
_____
_____

Something to Remember

16

Our Goal

Action plan

Our expectations

Date accomplished

The Story

Things we learned in the process

_____
_____
_____
_____
_____

Most cherished moment

_____
_____
_____
_____
_____

Something to Remember

17

Our Goal

Action plan

_____
_____
_____
_____
_____

Our expectations

_____
_____
_____
_____
_____

Date accomplished

_____

The Story

Things we learned in the process

_____
_____
_____
_____
_____
_____

Most cherished moment

_____
_____
_____
_____
_____
_____

Something to Remember

18

Our Goal

Action plan

Our expectations

Date accomplished

The Story

Things we learned in the process

_____
_____
_____
_____
_____

Most cherished moment

_____
_____
_____
_____
_____

Something to Remember

19

Our Goal

Action plan

_____
_____
_____
_____
_____
_____

Our expectations

_____
_____
_____
_____
_____
_____

Date accomplished

_____

The Story

Things we learned in the process

_____
_____
_____
_____
_____

Most cherished moment

_____
_____
_____
_____
_____

Something to Remember

20

Our Goal

Action plan

_____
_____
_____
_____
_____

Our expectations

_____
_____
_____
_____
_____

Date accomplished

_____

The Story

Things we learned in the process

_____
_____
_____
_____
_____

Most cherished moment

_____
_____
_____
_____
_____

Something to Remember

21

Our Goal

Action plan

Our expectations

Date accomplished

The Story

Things we learned in the process

_____
_____
_____
_____
_____

Most cherished moment

_____
_____
_____
_____
_____

Something to Remember

22

Our Goal

Action plan

Our expectations

Date accomplished

The Story

Things we learned in the process

_____
_____
_____
_____
_____

Most cherished moment

_____
_____
_____
_____
_____

Something to Remember

23

Our Goal

Action plan

Our expectations

Date accomplished

The Story

Things we learned in the process

_____
_____
_____
_____
_____

Most cherished moment

_____
_____
_____
_____
_____

Something to Remember

24

Our Goal

Action plan

Our expectations

Date accomplished

The Story

Things we learned in the process

_____
_____
_____
_____
_____

Most cherished moment

_____
_____
_____
_____
_____

Something to Remember

25

Our Goal

Action plan

Our expectations

Date accomplished

The Story

Things we learned in the process

_____
_____
_____
_____
_____

Most cherished moment

_____
_____
_____
_____
_____

Something to Remember

26

Our Goal

Action plan

Our expectations

Date accomplished

The Story

Things we learned in the process

_____
_____
_____
_____
_____

Most cherished moment

_____
_____
_____
_____
_____

Something to Remember

27

Our Goal

Action plan

Our expectations

Date accomplished

The Story

Things we learned in the process

_____
_____
_____
_____
_____

Most cherished moment

_____
_____
_____
_____
_____

Something to Remember

28

Action plan

Our expectations

Date accomplished

The Story

Things we learned in the process

_____

_____

_____

_____

_____

_____

Most cherished moment

_____

_____

_____

_____

_____

_____

Something to Remember

29

Our Goal

Action plan

_____
_____
_____
_____
_____

Our expectations

_____
_____
_____
_____
_____

Date accomplished

_____

The Story

Things we learned in the process

_____
_____
_____
_____
_____

Most cherished moment

_____
_____
_____
_____
_____

Something to Remember

30

Our Goal

Action plan

Our expectations

Date accomplished

The Story

Things we learned in the process

_____
_____
_____
_____
_____

Most cherished moment

_____
_____
_____
_____
_____

Something to Remember

31

Our Goal

Action plan

Our expectations

Date accomplished

The Story

Things we learned in the process

_____
_____
_____
_____
_____

Most cherished moment

_____
_____
_____
_____
_____

Something to Remember

32

Our Goal

Action plan

Our expectations

Date accomplished

The Story

Things we learned in the process

_____
_____
_____
_____
_____

Most cherished moment

_____
_____
_____
_____
_____

Something to Remember

33

Our Goal

Action plan

_____
_____
_____
_____
_____

Our expectations

_____
_____
_____
_____
_____

Date accomplished

_____

The Story

Things we learned in the process

_____
_____
_____
_____
_____

Most cherished moment

_____
_____
_____
_____
_____

Something to Remember

34

Our Goal

Action plan

Our expectations

Date accomplished

The Story

Things we learned in the process

_____
_____
_____
_____
_____

Most cherished moment

_____
_____
_____
_____
_____

Something to Remember

35

Our Goal

Action plan

_____
_____
_____
_____
_____

Our expectations

_____
_____
_____
_____
_____

Date accomplished

_____

The Story

Things we learned in the process

_____
_____
_____
_____
_____

Most cherished moment

_____
_____
_____
_____
_____

Something to Remember

36

Our Goal

Action plan

Our expectations

Date accomplished

The Story

Things we learned in the process

_____
_____
_____
_____
_____

Most cherished moment

_____
_____
_____
_____
_____

Something to Remember

37

Our Goal

Action plan

_____
_____
_____
_____
_____

Our expectations

_____
_____
_____
_____
_____

Date accomplished

_____

The Story

Things we learned in the process

_____
_____
_____
_____
_____

Most cherished moment

_____
_____
_____
_____
_____

Something to Remember

38

Our Goal

Action plan

Our expectations

Date accomplished

The Story

Things we learned in the process

_____
_____
_____
_____
_____

Most cherished moment

_____
_____
_____
_____
_____

Something to Remember

39

Our Goal

Action plan

Our expectations

Date accomplished

The Story

Things we learned in the process

_____
_____
_____
_____
_____

Most cherished moment

_____
_____
_____
_____
_____

Something to Remember

40

Our Goal

Action plan

_____
_____
_____
_____
_____

Our expectations

_____
_____
_____
_____
_____

Date accomplished

_____

The Story

Things we learned in the process

_____
_____
_____
_____
_____

Most cherished moment

_____
_____
_____
_____
_____

Something to Remember

41

Our Goal

Action plan

_____
_____
_____
_____
_____

Our expectations

_____
_____
_____
_____
_____

Date accomplished

_____

The Story

Things we learned in the process

_____
_____
_____
_____
_____

Most cherished moment

_____
_____
_____
_____
_____

Something to Remember

42

Our Goal

Action plan

Our expectations

Date accomplished

The Story

Things we learned in the process

_____
_____
_____
_____
_____

Most cherished moment

_____
_____
_____
_____
_____

Something to Remember

43

Our Goal

Action plan

Our expectations

Date accomplished

The Story

Things we learned in the process

_____
_____
_____
_____
_____

Most cherished moment

_____
_____
_____
_____
_____

Something to Remember

Our Goal

Action plan

Our expectations

Date accomplished

The Story

Things we learned in the process

_____
_____
_____
_____
_____

Most cherished moment

_____
_____
_____
_____
_____

Something to Remember

45

Our Goal

Action plan

_____
_____
_____
_____
_____

Our expectations

_____
_____
_____
_____
_____

Date accomplished

_____

The Story

Things we learned in the process

_____
_____
_____
_____
_____

Most cherished moment

_____
_____
_____
_____
_____

Something to Remember

46

Our Goal

Action plan

Our expectations

Date accomplished

The Story

Things we learned in the process

_____
_____
_____
_____
_____
_____

Most cherished moment

_____
_____
_____
_____
_____
_____

Something to Remember

47

Our Goal

Action plan

Our expectations

Date accomplished

The Story

Things we learned in the process

_____
_____
_____
_____
_____

Most cherished moment

_____
_____
_____
_____
_____

Something to Remember

48

Our Goal

Action plan

Our expectations

Date accomplished

The Story

Things we learned in the process

_____
_____
_____
_____
_____
_____

Most cherished moment

_____
_____
_____
_____
_____
_____

Something to Remember

49

Our Goal

Action plan

Our expectations

Date accomplished

The Story

Things we learned in the process

_____
_____
_____
_____
_____

Most cherished moment

_____
_____
_____
_____
_____

Something to Remember

50

Our Goal

Action plan

_____
_____
_____
_____
_____

Our expectations

_____
_____
_____
_____
_____

Date accomplished

_____

The Story

Things we learned in the process

_____
_____
_____
_____
_____

Most cherished moment

_____
_____
_____
_____
_____

Something to Remember

Congratulations!

You've made it to the end!

Looking Back

Quite a few fulfilling days, great memories, and one-of-a-kind experiences later! Hopefully, you've now completed most of your bucket list items, if not all, and you are ready to look back at your amazing journey. Discuss the following questions to reflect, reminisce, and make an overall evaluation of your adventures together.

1. Which bucket list goal was the easiest and which one the hardest to achieve?

2. How did pursuing your goals change your relationship dynamics?

3. Which bucket list item proved to be the most exciting?

4. What is the most important thing you learned through your bucket list journey?

5. What was the most challenging part of your bucket list adventures?

6. Which bucket list item did you have the most fun with?

7. Was there any goal that was easier to achieve than you expected? If so, which one was it?

8. On a scale of 1 to 10, how rewarding was the completion of your bucket list?

9. Did you try anything out of your comfort zone? If so, how did it feel?

10. How likely are you to set new goals and create another shared bucket list in the near future?